GOD AND
HANDICAPPE

Selected papers presented at the joint conference of the International Congress of Christian Physicians and the Innere Mission und Hilfswerk der Evangelischen Kirchen, Dresden, April 1981.

PUBLISHED FOR THE
INTERNATIONAL CONGRESS OF CHRISTIAN PHYSICIANS
BY

 CHRISTIAN MEDICAL FELLOWSHIP
PUBLICATIONS
LONDON

© Christian Medical Fellowship

First published 1982

ISBN 0 906747 07 4

Christian Medical Fellowship
157 Waterloo Road, London SE1 8XN

Made and printed in Great Britain by
Stanley L. Hunt (Printers) Ltd., Rushden, Northants.

INTRODUCTION

The United Nations Organization designated 1981 as the International Year of Disabled People—not as a year in which to fuss over the handicapped and then to forget them, but as a time in which to take stock of what has been done in the past and to consider what can and should be done in the future. Realizing that this was very much the concern of Christian doctors, the International Congress of Christian Physicians (ICCP) gladly accepted a proposal to join with colleagues associated with the *Innere Mission* of the Lutheran Church of East Germany in a conference on 'God's Response to the Handicapped'.

As a result, some 130 participants from 14 countries, nearly all of whom were doctors, met in Dresden, East Germany, in April 1981. There they shared their technical knowledge and discussed how they applied their Christian insights to their service to the handicapped in every aspect of disability—physical, mental and spiritual.

For the ICCP this was an innovation, being not only a conference held in an Eastern bloc country, but also the first collaborative meeting with another Christian organization. Since its first meeting in Amsterdam in 1963 the ICCP has met at regular three-year intervals in Oxford, Oslo, Toronto, Singapore and Davos. The object of these meetings has been to encourage (1) the gathering together of representatives from national Christian medical fellowships and societies for their mutual benefit, strengthening and exchange of ideas, and (2) the formation of fellowships and societies in countries where none exists at present. This pattern of conferences has recently been changed to a four-yearly cycle in order to permit time for regional conferences to take place in the intervening years. This has given rise to meetings in Greece, South America and, in 1981, in East Germany.

For those who were privileged to attend and participate, the Dresden meeting was a truly memorable occasion and experience. Shortly after his return Dr. Ronald Winton wrote: 'Those of us who came from the West felt the warmth, and indeed the eagerness, of the welcome from our Eastern European colleagues.... Undoubtedly it was a time of encouragement for them, but many of us found that they ministered to us rather than we to them.'

These words express succinctly the mood and feelings of many from the West at that conference, and it is hoped that the reader of these pages, too, will capture something of that experience and challenge.

This booklet contains two of the papers that were presented at Dresden together with a résumé of a third. Mr. Richard Cook, an English paediatric surgeon, makes it clear that the management of infants with congenital

3

malformations is not only a matter of applying clinical and technical skills to a physical problem, but also of caring for people.   Dr. Jürgen Trogisch shows his deep insights into mental handicap from his experience with mentally retarded children at the Katharinenhof, Grosshennersdorf, a rehabilitation centre of the *Innere Mission* of the Lutheran Church in Saxony.   Spiritual handicap, the third aspect, is one which concerns us all, and this is dealt with by Dr. Ronald Winton, formerly Editor of the Medical Journal of Australia.

CONTENTS

Page

THE DEFORMED CHILD—WHO CARES?—*Richard Cook*   7

CONGENITAL SUBNORMALITY: THE REHABILITATION OF THE
SEVERELY MENTALLY HANDICAPPED—*Jürgen Trogisch*   27

REAL MAN THROUGH GOD'S GRACE—*Ronald Winton*   47

THE DEFORMED CHILD—WHO CARES?

RICHARD C. M. COOK, M.A., F.R.C.S.

Paediatric Surgeon, The Royal Liverpool Children's Hospital and Alder Hey Children's Hospital.

The Deformed Child—who cares?

I began to prepare this paper on the first day of 1981, the International Year of Disabled People. News items on television and radio, and reports in newspapers and magazines, have ensured that the plight of the disabled has been kept well in the public eye. The BBC Television children's programme, Blue Peter, has raised a large sum of money for the purchase of equipment for the disabled, and many other fund-raising activities have been undertaken during the year. All this has revealed a genuine concern for the disabled, but this concern is matched by a lack of knowledge, compounded by prejudice, embarrassment, horror and shame. The International Year has focused attention on disablement and has held up handicap as a challenge to the whole of society.

Yet in all the publicity there has been little emphasis on the child born disabled, although it is estimated[1] that an abnormal baby is born into the world every 30 seconds. Only one-third of structural defects are easily detected at birth, while others will come to light later. The Liverpool Congenital Anomalies Register has, for over 20 years, been collecting comprehensive statistics concerning infants born in Liverpool and Bootle. The total incidence of anomalous infants has ranged between 25 and 42 per thousand total births.[2] Many of the anomalies recorded are trivial, but 20-25 per thousand total births have malformations that are sufficient to cause death or severe handicap, or to require surgery. Congenital malformations may be classified as structural, functional, metabolic, behavioural and so forth. Sometimes one anomaly falls into several groups and an individual child's problems may extend right across the spectrum. In this paper, as in my daily work, while I am dealing primarily with structural defects, I cannot ignore their functional, behavioural, hereditary, and other implications.

In the last 100 years there has been a ninefold decrease in infant mortality, largely due to better control of infection and the grosser metabolic disturbances. Congenital malformations have become of increasing numerical importance and now account for 20% of all neonatal deaths. While surgery can reduce this toll, some of those operated on cannot be cured, and life for them, despite all that medical science may offer, will be short or disabled or both.

Words such as 'disabled' and 'handicapped' are useful descriptive terms whose broadness of meaning is sometimes valuable, but at other times becomes a barrier to understanding. There are dangers in applying labels to people, for the label can become a stereotype[3] with which we categorize a group of people, assume that they are all identical with each other, and regard

9

them, therefore, as different from and separated from us. Leprosy, cancer, mongolism, handicap—these are all words that can help to identify those in need of special help. All too often they are words that build barriers and separate 'them' from 'us'.

Who cares about a deformed child? My impression is that many people care, and the increased public awareness of all handicapped people has had at least two results. The first is that society is accepting greater responsibility for the provision of improved facilities, from simple items such as the design of access to public buildings to matters of education, training and employment. The second is that we, as doctors, are questioning what we do in the management of handicap, and even more in its prevention. It is this audit of our activities that we often find threatening, yet ideally it should provide guidance and support.

Ian Kennedy, in his Reith Lectures,[4] contended that medical ethics were much too important to leave to doctors. While we may agree that ethics are of great importance, are we prepared to put as much faith as he does in the reliability of public opinion? It may well be that our conscience demands that we do not simply follow public opinion, nor is it often wise or useful simply to oppose it in single-handed confrontation. We certainly have a responsibility to make known the principles which we believe to be true and right for our society, and thus help to shape public opinion on those matters in which our training and experience give us a measure of professional expertise.

So-called public opinion comes to us not only in provocative Reith Lectures, but also in the opinions and demands of our patients or their relatives, or of various groups campaigning on their behalf. There is an increasingly critical view of what we as doctors are doing, but it should be remembered that it may be society and not medicine that has taken the wrong turning.[5] The paternalism that has dominated the attitude of doctor and patient alike is being challenged by an attitude of 'consumerism'. John Ladd pointed out in *The Lancet*[6] that paternalism dates at least from Plato, who numbered the doctor among his 'philosopher rulers'. As such, the doctor had absolute authority over sick people. Consumerism is founded on the idea that the patient knows best, and medicine is a commodity to be dispensed on demand. But who does know best what is right? Maybe my subject is wrongly titled, for the problem is not so much 'Who cares?' as 'Who cares best?' How is real care expressed when we are faced with a newborn infant with a congenital malformation?

THE NATURE OF THE PROBLEM

Congenital malformations are not a newly discovered phenomenon. Asshurbanipal (680-626 BC) was an unusual Assyrian king in that he was more of a scholar than a soldier and his Kuyunjik library of cuneiform tablets at Nineveh was a collection from many centuries before his own time. Some of

10

its documents[7] detail the obvious external malformations that were of such interest not only to the ancient cultures of Mesopotamia, but also to the Greeks and the Romans, because such a birth was a portent or warning of future misfortune—hence the word 'monster' (from Latin, *monere*, to warn), a word which has now gained a very different connotation.

Our ancestors were not slow to find, or invent, causes for abnormalities in the newborn. The theory of maternal impressions was certainly extant several thousand years ago, as we know from the description of Jacob's sheep-breeding techniques.[8] Spartan women were encouraged to gaze at statues of Castor and Pollux to ensure that they bore handsome strong sons. Montaigne considered it beyond dispute that women 'impart the marks of their fancy to the bodies of the children they bear in their wombs'.[1]

The idea that such children were the product of cross fertilization with animals (or even spirits) seemed to be accepted without imputing guilt in ancient Indian and Egyptian cultures, but in the dark Middle Ages this idea led to the persecution of child and mother, and even up to the 17th century many were put to death by an outraged society. Even the men did not escape these now obviously unjust laws, for the story is recorded[9] that the birth of a cyclopic pig in 1641 in the Colony and Plantation of New Haven brought about the execution of George Spencer, a one-eyed servant.

Death has been a widely practised means of dealing with malformed neonates, for example by leaving them exposed on a hillside or seashore, or throwing them over cliffs. To the Greeks and Romans this was a simple economic expediency in relation to any unwanted birth. Plato advocated it for his ideal republic. The Spartans practised it not only on the puny and ill-shaped but also on those who did not appear positively healthy and vigorous. Professor and Mrs. Illingworth's book *Lessons from Childhood* would be slimmer, and the world would have been poorer, if some of the sickly infants they describe had been so treated.[10]

In our own country's recent past the malformed neonate represented only a small proportion of the handicapped and disabled, and there was little effective treatment available to any. The family bore the burden as well as it could, and for many of the children who survived begging was the only means of keeping alive. Various voluntary societies stemmed from the pioneering work of individuals who saw the desperate need of their day and met it with a compassion learned from their Master. The Shaftesbury Society, Müller's Orphanages and Dr. Barnardo's are among the best known organizations that grew out of the realization by Christian people of their responsibility to the poor and the disadvantaged.

However, it is not now simply a case of caring for the small residue who survive. The application of medical science has increased the number of survivors, and many are asking if it has done enough to improve the quality of survival.

How each generation, in its turn, deals with its malformed infants depends

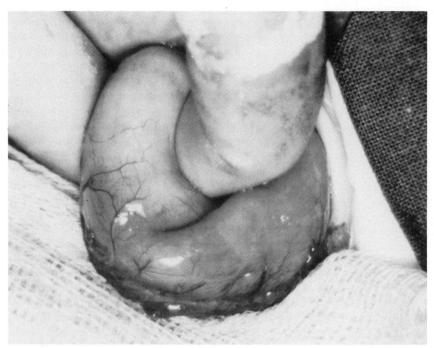

Fig. 1. A pyloric 'tumour' carried a mortality rate of 50% in the 1930s.

on at least three things: firstly its understanding of the causes of those malformations, secondly its technical, medical and surgical ability to treat them, and thirdly its view of the value of human life. There have been considerable changes in all three spheres but it is the last two that will occupy my thoughts here—the responsible use of our sophisticated medical and surgical skills in relation to our appraisal of the value of human life.

New surgical techniques have been developed and are constantly being improved. We sometimes need to remind ourselves of the advantages of our modern age. Death from pyloric stenosis in infants is now almost unheard of in main centres; in the 1930s the mortality rate was 50% (Fig. 1). Before 1946 no infant with oesophageal atresia survived; nowadays death in an infant of good birth weight and with no complications is a rare event. We also have a far greater understanding of the physiology of the newborn infant, and especially the immature or dysmature. The contributions of pathologist, radiologist and anaesthetist have been, and still are, immense.

Returning to the conflicting attitudes of 'consumerism' and 'paternalism' in medicine, within the discipline of paediatric surgery it may be difficult to know who is the consumer. The law invests the parents with the power and responsibility of giving consent, but action or inaction in relation to an infant

12

will have far-reaching consequences, not only for the parents, but more so for the child and to a lesser extent for siblings, friends, neighbours and society.

Again, however much we may theorize about paternalism and consumerism, there is no doubt that in practice we, as doctors, have great power—power entrusted to us by our patients or their relatives—and at crucial moments I find myself painfully aware of my power to persuade a parent to consent to almost anything.

There are times when I can wield this power with great confidence that it really is for the benefit of all concerned. The commonest congenital anomaly I deal with is undoubtedly the inguinal hernia—so trivial that we hardly classify it as a malformation. If it is ignored in the small infant, there is a considerable risk of incarceration, testicular infarction, intestinal obstruction and even death. A relatively simple procedure, with the infant in hospital for a day, with his mother beside him in all his waking moments, enables us to discharge him safe and sound with nothing more than a tiny scar which itself will be virtually undetectable in a few months.

There are other occasions when I cannot be quite so sure of the entirely beneficial result of my recommended treatment. David is the first baby of a young couple in North Wales. He was born a little prematurely and transferred to Liverpool with the diagnosis of oesophageal atresia. We found that he also had a minor anal anomaly. It was not difficult to explain to his father that both these items could be operated on with reasonable expectation of normal healthy growth and development to follow. In my own mind I had slight reservations, for the child with corrected oesophageal atresia is liable later to have problems with swallowing and, perhaps more importantly, with breathing. He will not be a respiratory cripple but he is unlikely to become an Olympic sprinter. The operation went smoothly, but subsequent investigation showed that David has only a single ectopic kidney, and at one year of age the marginal adequacy of his renal function has been demonstrated by the major upset caused by what are usually minor episodes of diarrhoea or vomiting. A question mark stands against David's future.

What, though, am I to recommend to parents when I know that the future cannot be easy, and that survival will inevitably be associated with major handicaps? The infant born with a myelomeningocele and some degree of paraplegia is the obvious example to take, but we face a similar dilemma with the infant with Down's syndrome and duodenal atresia, or meconium ileus and presumptive cystic fibrosis.

The spina bifida baby has become something of a *cause célèbre* and many voices are raised telling us what we should and should not do. The loudest voices often belong to those with the least involvement, and opinions are often expressed in emotional terms. 'It is easy to forget that . . . (they) will grow up into large and monstrous adolescents and eventually into totally unmanageable adults.'[11] Such a sweeping generalization based on hard cases indicates a serious loss of perspective, and though the advice may be couched in high moral tones of deep concern, it undermines the age-old principle of compassionate care in medicine, not only for the most vulnerable neonate but by logical extension for the handicapped and disabled of any age.

The correctness of any decision about either medical or surgical treatment depends on a number of factors. First and foremost we need to be able to make an accurate and honest prognosis. Hippocrates is credited with saying that the best doctor is the one who can foretell his patient's future accurately, rather than ease his symptoms at the present. Prognosis must include not only the natural history of the condition if left untreated, but also the results of the treatments that are available. Much muddled thinking, and conflicting opinions about the prognosis of the infant with spina bifida, have clouded the ethical issues and befogged the view of those trying to make decisions in the child's best interest.

The first common misconception is that modern medical practice is responsible for the survival of children born with myelomeningoceles. My first contact with spina bifida patients was as a medical student in the 1950s, seeing adults who had survived without surgical intervention. Some 5-10% of those born before then survived to adult life and 40% survived at least 18 months. The 1960s saw the introduction of more effective treatment for hydrocephalus, and this, combined with early surgery to the back, led to the survival of nearly 50% of affected children,[12] some with major mental and physical handicaps that were more of a challenge to the child than to the surgeon. Thus there arose the second misconception that is so frequently voiced, that the quality of life is accurately predictable and its value measurable.

The results of a review recently carried out in Liverpool,[13] while leaving no room for complacency, are not entirely without hope for the young adult who has been born with spina bifida. Of 178 infants operated on in 1963/64 87 survivors (43%) who are now aged 16 or 17 years were assessed. Nine are very severely handicapped, mentally or physically or both. Twenty are independent and considered capable of normal employment. Fifty-eight have problems with continence and/or locomotion. Twenty-three of these need personal help at home and the other 35, though socially independent, will need sheltered employment.

In an attempt to concentrate the surgical and medical care on those children who would most benefit, and to protect from unnecessary suffering those who would not, John Lorber of the Department of Paediatrics of the University of Sheffield published an analysis of the results of treatment and advocated the careful selection of children for surgery.[14] Certain criteria (paraplegia, gross hydrocephalus, kyphosis and other major anomalies) were used as contraindications for immediate operation.[15] It is not difficult, nor is it hard on the conscience, to select out that small group, perhaps 10%, in whom early death will occur because of intracranial haemorrhage, respiratory problems or associated uncorrectable anomalies. Immediate surgery and complex medical support are not applied because they will be ineffective. Compassionate care of the infant is all that anyone can usefully provide. Nor is it difficult to select for early surgical care the infants with minimal handicap and a small lesion. Operation, if done early and successfully, will not only preserve neurological function and quality of life, but also decreases the chances of meningoventriculitis, with its associated risk of death or brain damage[16] (Fig. 2).

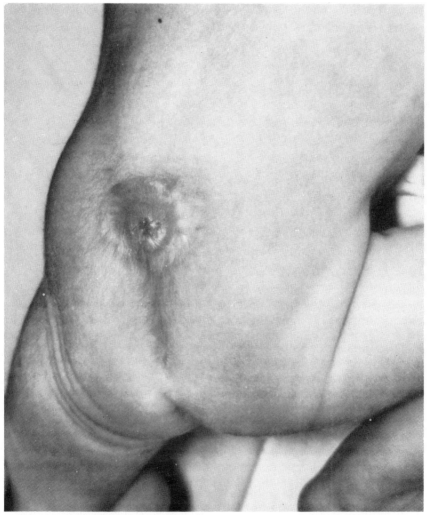

Fig. 2. Myelomeningocele: the small lesion, potentially lethal or handicapping if infection occurs. This child is now a virtually normal ten year old.

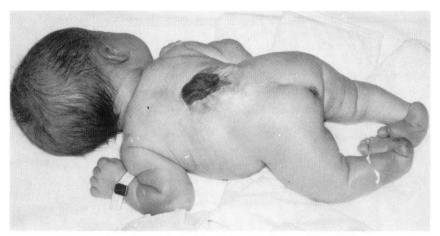

Fig. 3. A newborn infant with a thoracolumbar myelomeningocele, paraplegia, kyphosis and hydrocephalus. Withholding surgery does not necessarily mean early death.

A considerable number of infants will, however, still pose a dilemma because they have some of Lorber's adverse criteria, and survival will be associated with handicap—perhaps mental as well as physical. All too often the dilemma is considered[17] to be solved by withholding surgery on the assumption that this is synonymous with early death (Fig. 3). In the experience of many centres this has not been found to be true unless death is accelerated by sedation and withholding of food. In our own experience in Liverpool my surgical colleagues and I, supported by the neurologists, have attempted to make an early assessment of each new referral. We often do not recommend immediate back closure if there is no function in the legs or if other adverse criteria apply. Ordinary care continues—food, rest, comfort and love—often given by the parents at home rather than by the nursing staff in the hospital. We have shown that some 30% of these infants survive for a year or more without any special medical or surgical treatment,[18] and need to be considered for surgery during this period on the basis of the normal indications for such treatment in any patient. In our experience this delay has not meant any increase in the degree of disability of these particular children.

There are thus practical problems in determining the form of treatment that will be best in relation to each child born with a myelomeningocele, for no two are the same. Strenuous application of all available therapy to all such infants will give a survival rate of over 50%. Many of these may have a very poor quality of life and be dependent on repeated surgery and other therapy. No treatment for any would allow the death, or cause increased disability, of some whose quality of life after surgery could be expected to be excellent. A

16

middle way is, I consider, possible and best. The precise indications for early surgical intervention are, I believe, becoming clearer. The real problem is what to do with the infants to whom immediate operation is not offered. Some will die at an early stage, but others have a firm hold on life and will not easily let go.

I have tried to highlight some of the practical problems facing those involved in the management of the infant with a congenital malformation. Let us now ask ourselves if there is any fundamental ethical system that will help in decision-making—not only for the infant with spina bifida, but for any infant with a disabling congenital malformation.

A BIBLICAL BASIS FOR DECISION

I am sometimes tempted to ask why God has not made the answer to our problems clearer, and to complain that he has left us to search out solutions from the apparent obscurity of Scripture. I find, however, that Scripture does have things to say about the unborn, about children, about the handicapped and about human life. We are not given precise rules or a code of conduct, for this would be suited only to a particular time and place. Rather we are given principles that provide the foundation and basis of behaviour, together with some rules which illustrate, but can never exhaust, the principle.[19]

I am immediately aware[20] that this view stands diametrically opposed to the ideas of the proponents of situational ethics—ideas which have always been around but which have been popularized on the Continent by men such as Barth, Bonhoeffer and Bultmann, in the United States by Joseph Fletcher and in Britain by John Robinson. They would apparently regard the timeless principles of which I spoke as relative or provisional rather than binding. They have, it would seem, dispensed with the authority of God's law and replaced it with 'love'. It must be admitted that a hard pharisaical legalism has often driven love far from the application of law to the difficult dilemmas that surround so many of our human relationships. Their re-emphasis of love is therefore welcome, but the abandonment of all rules leaves many perplexed. This is especially so in situations where an act is done which would normally be considered wrong (such as killing a baby) but where the motive is love (to save the child from suffering). Fletcher claims[21] that such a deed is 'not excusably evil, it is positively good'.

If love is to be the only determining principle of all our actions, how are we to know how to love? To make love replace law does not ease decision-making; it takes away the yardstick by which we can assess our actions, for love in scriptural terms is obedience to God's law: 'If you love me, you will keep my commandments' (John 14. 15) and, 'By this we know that we love the children of God, when we love God and keep his commandments' (1 John 5. 2). This seems to be a much surer springboard for action.

Probably the most important principle is derived from the statement that God made man as the pinnacle of his creative activity in the world. The manner in which we were made is unimportant; the fact of it is vital, as is the often-repeated statement that man is made in God's image. Many have been the explanations of this, but the clearest I have come across compares the process to the reduction of a breathtaking scenic view to a small photograph or simple painting, or the rewriting of a great orchestral work for a piano, so that man is 'a transcription of the eternal, incorporeal Creator in terms of temporal, bodily, creaturely existence'.[22]

The Bible has hardly made mention of the wonder and greatness of God's initial work, however, when the tragedy is introduced. In the very act of making a creature who had the freedom to love and serve and obey, the possibility of rejection and rebellion was inevitably present; and so the Fall. This crisis was clearly not just a moral, spiritual failure, but involved the totality, the wholeness of man. Physical degeneration, decay and death were among the consequences. The image of God in man was not eradicated even though it was damaged, and the Bible stresses that the image of God in man remains, albeit at times hard to see. Now this image, this likeness, implies dignity and worth, destiny and freedom. Thus each individual has personality, and we should beware of the prejudiced stereotyping of groups of our fellow human beings. Each individual has worth, or value, and shares with me the right to justice and brotherhood.

One fact in particular needs to be emphasized in the current debate: humanity is not a goal to be achieved; it is a status conferred. My humanity is not based on my holding of a certificate confirming that I contribute to the community's economic welfare, or have achieved an appropriate score in tests of emotional activities or appreciative responses. Humanity is a personal identity that reflects some small part of the Person of God himself.

Against the background of these great truths—of man's initial perfection and great worth, and of his current struggle with the numerous results of his rejection of his Creator's authority—we find some interesting examples of handicapped people in the Bible. Two aspects seem to emerge. On the one hand disease, blemish and malformation illustrate not just the depths to which man has sunk, but also the totality of the salvation that God is working out for men. In Leviticus[23] we see that any such disability cuts off the sufferer from the temple rituals, for nothing that is so patently imperfect can stand in God's presence. But the day will come when the lame will not be banished from God's kingdom but will be gathered in and made the stock of a strong nation,[24] infant mortality will be non-existent,[25] while the cured cripple follows into the temple leaping and dancing and praising God.[26]

As well as providing illustrations of the miracle of wholeness restored, the Bible also shows handicap as an opportunity for demonstrating the care that should spring from our common humanity. Mephibosheth, lame in his feet after an accident in childhood,[27] became the object of David's long continued care and love, although custom would have suggested that he could have killed him as the grandson of his defeated enemy Saul. Christ specifically told the socially over-conscious Pharisee to ask as guests to his home 'the poor, the crippled, the lame and the blind'. He continued this train of thought into the parable of the great banquet: the men of apparently great worth will not taste any of it, for the places round the table will be filled with the 'poor, the crippled, the blind and the lame' gathered in from the streets and alleys.[28]

PRACTICAL OUTCOME

In the light of such attitudes in Scripture, how do we see our responsibilities towards the newborn infant with malformation?

First and foremost, as a weak and vulnerable member of society he is deserving of our utmost care and attention. This care and attention must clearly be directed to helping him fulfil his potentialities both for survival and for the experiences and activities that make up the complex tapestry of a human life.

His potentiality for survival may not be great. Indeed it may be clear that even with complicated and prolonged treatment life will be short. No one would seriously suggest that the doctor must struggle to achieve a few more days of life at any cost, but, conversely, I would contend that we cannot put ourselves in the position of judging any child as having a quality of life so poor as not to merit survival. The care that any newborn dependent infant is normally afforded must be given to all, while medical and surgical measures are used, on the basis of correct indications, to relieve suffering and to minimize handicap. My fellow paediatric surgeons in Liverpool and the paediatric neurologists who cooperate with us in the management of spina bifida and hydrocephalus (although not all specifically committed to a Christian ethic) have not considered heavy sedation and the withholding of food to be an option that is open to us. Such action, though apparently based on compassion, not only denies the unique and unpredictable value of human life, but fails to recognize that real love cannot run counter to moral principles. As stated earlier, the precise indications for early surgical intervention in infants with spina bifida are becoming clearer. Even if surgery is not indicated at first, it cannot be assumed that there is nothing constructive that can be done later, and in the infant whose zest for life is clear efforts must be directed to minimizing the disabilities with which he is growing up.

Ian Kennedy in his Reith Lectures[4] complained that doctors are trained to be solvers and not carers. Our education has given us disease-orientated ideas which always demand a specific response to fix the part rather than to treat the whole. Perhaps in neonatal surgery more than in most other branches of medicine it is vital to take an unblinkered view of the entire scene and to care for the whole rather than simply treat a part.

Good care of the infant with a malformation must start with the realization that it is rarely within the competence of a single individual. It involves a

19

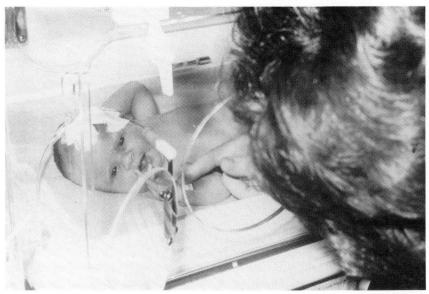

Fig. 4.   Another source of strength for a sick baby.

Fig. 5.   Attendance at the local school is often to the benefit of both the
handicapped and their normal peers.

team and the most important members of that team are the parents. The first and most crucial steps are therefore the initial explanation of the problems and the prompt involvement of the parents in the infant's care. Much has been written[1] [29] [30] and said about the clumsy incompetence with which the news is first broken, and which can have such far-reaching effects. This has been carefully studied in relation to mental handicap but less so in relation to physical malformations. Many of the problems are common to both—the grief reaction and mourning for the 'lost normal child' they expected may lead to guilt, rejection, marital disharmony and a variety of other responses. Unhurried, sympathetic and often repetitive interviews are needed.

Immediate contact between mother and infant is necessary[31] [32] since neonatal separation will add to the mother's feelings of guilt and uselessness, will increase the risks of rejection and add to the child's sufferings (Fig. 4). Sometimes we are guilty of working hard to show parents that a child is a human, dependent individual without allowing them the opportunity to be dependable. Whatever benefits the technicalities of surgery may bring to an infant, to be rejected will in itself be a handicap, and it is clear that the disabled infant and child will be infinitely better off as a member of a natural family than in an institution, however good the latter may be.

Much of this is applicable whatever the malformation and disability and however long or short life is expected to be. When survival is likely, and if the parents have the opportunity to voice their fears, they often look far ahead, trying to anticipate the effect of their child's handicap on his life at school, his prospects for employment, marriage, recreation and so on. Special schools will always be necessary for some, but the provision of some assistance often allows even quite severely handicapped children to attend their local schools in the ordinary way, to the benefit both of themselves and their more normal peers[33] [34] (Fig. 5). Financial payments for handicap have been suggested as one way of providing help for an individual or his family in meeting the extra costs involved in living. But the need is not simply for material things, but for family-orientated support[37] which will enable the parents to cope with their own shattered emotions, with one another, and with the rest of the family. Unless the parents can cope with the strain, family break-up is likely, and the tragedy of a malformed birth extends far more widely than just to the individual child.

It is not only the problems of this particular malformed infant that may cause concern to the parents. They will often ask at quite an early stage about the risks of the recurrence of a disorder in future pregnancies. The initial talk with the parents may involve specific questions about family history and logically lead to genetic counselling. While some general reassurances or warnings may be in order, I try to make sure that the parents can have an unhurried discussion about the causes and risks, and the possibility of prevention, at a later and calmer moment.

However, I am painfully aware that I usually have little to tell them

21

specifically about why their baby has exomphalos, an anorectal anomaly or spina bifida. The most I can usually do is to quote some very general statistics, try to banish feelings of guilt (the ancient and mediaeval theory of maternal impressions lives on in many mothers' and grandmothers' minds), and perhaps suggest some measures that may minimize the risks in future pregnancies. This moves us into the realms of prevention of malformations, which clearly has important ethical overtones depending on whether we are preventing conception or birth.

Recent evidence [38] [39] that vitamin supplements may help to reduce the incidence of the conception of infants with neural tube defects (myelomeningocele and anencephaly) is clearly exciting, even if not fully proved in some people's view. Such therapy may provide a safe and healthy environment and adequate nutrition for the early stages of embryogenesis and is in the best traditions of preventative medicine.

The fetus with a neural tube defect can, however, be detected (reasonably accurately and with a small complication rate) fairly early in pregnancy. A number of chromosomal disorders and metabolic diseases can also be diagnosed. The B.M.A. *Handbook on Medical Ethics*[40] points out that screening (for disease at all ages—not just prenatally) causes a dilemma because it reveals 'sick persons who do not, at present, seek medical help'. In

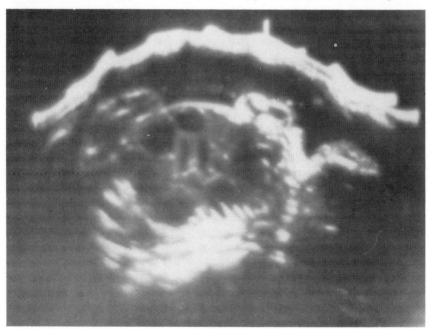

Fig. 6. Ultrasound scan in late pregnancy may have a positive value when it reveals dilated loops of intestine later found to be due to ileal atresia.

22

relation to the fetus the 'help' offered is most likely to be abortion, though there are occasional instances where the value of screening may be more positive, as, for instance, when ultrasound examination reveals an intestinal obstruction (Fig. 6) and arrangements for surgery can begin shortly before birth.

There is nothing to be gained in making most prenatal diagnoses if the parents are not agreeable in principle beforehand to termination of the pregnancy if the tests prove positive. The effect of such an abortion on the parents' attitude to an already existing malformed child, or to one who 'slips through the net', and his attitude to the parents who might similarly have got rid of him, raises interesting but as yet unanswered questions.[41] [42]

Genetic disease and counselling can occasionally raise unnecessary fears of gross alterations of the gene frequency occurring because of the efforts of paediatric surgeons. The possible increase in the incidence of Hirschsprung's disease, pyloric stenosis, and other diseases with a familial basis are occasionally overstated. We are all too familiar with the ill-founded eugenic policies practised in Nazi Germany that were themselves the morally distorted offspring of earlier fears that the insane and feebleminded would so multiply that they would be a threat to normal society.[43]

The management of future pregnancies, and our attitude to termination of the life of the malformed (but viable) fetus, are not just theoretical problems for those of us concerned with the management of the abnormal or sick neonate. The difference between a fetus and an infant is one of maturity rather than of essential nature. A cavalier attitude to life before birth leads to devaluation of life at all ages.

Good and consistent care, for as long as necessary, must be the guiding principle in our approach to the handicapped and malformed of any age, and good care cannot be the deliberate ending of that life, nor can it be the artificial prolongation of existence. Careful attention to each of the problems of the deformed person may well alleviate not only the suffering but also much of the handicapping effect of disability. The handicapped themselves often have a much more optimistic attitude towards their disabilities than their professional assessors, and they are often willing to try their hand at far more ambitious projects than we give them credit for (Fig. 7). The disabled person is often quick to point out that his limited life is better than no life, but this cannot be taken as a licence to extend life at all costs.

I have attempted to define the principles which I try to apply to my professional decisions—decisions which are often not easy to make, which weigh heavily on me, and the results of which I have to live with in my professional life, even though the burden which some children and their families carry is infinitely heavier. The choice before us is often between two evils rather than between a clearly good and bad course. I am sure that I have made mistakes—that I have been overzealous in treatment on occasions when good care might have produced a shorter but less distressed life, and that

23

Fig. 7.   The handicapped often have a more optimistic attitude to their disabilities than their professional advisers.

I have omitted treatment that would have prolonged a worthwhile life. I trust that constant reappraisal of the results of my treatment will help me to make fewer mistakes in the future, and I trust too that I shall hold on to what I consider to be fundamental and vital principles, namely, that each human being, however weak and insignificant, is an individual of importance and value, whose life must not be deliberately shortened, but whose disabilities must be minimized and whose suffering relieved. How to balance these two sometimes contradictory duties is the challenge for all who care for the deformed child.

References

1 Fletcher, John (1974) 'Attitudes towards defective newborns' in *Problems of Birth Defects*, Ed. T. V. N. Persaud. MTP Press Ltd., Lancaster, pp. 373-384.
2 From data supplied by Professor Frank Harris.
3 Lindesmith, A. R., Strauss, A. L. and Denzin, N. K. (1975) *Social Psychology*. Dryden Press, Eastbourne.
4 Kennedy, I. (1980) *Unmasking Medicine; The Reith Lectures*. BBC Publications, London.
5 Humphries, R. (1981) Unmasking the Reith Lectures. *World Medicine*, *16*, 34-38.
6 Ladd, J. (1980) Who knows best? *Lancet*, *2*, 1127.
7 Warkany, J. (1959) Congenital malformations in the past. *J. Chron. Dis.*, *10*, 84-96.
8 Genesis 31. 37ff.
9 Hoadley, C. J. (Ed.) (1857) *Records of the Colony and Plantation of New Haven from 1638 to 1649*. Case, Tiffany and Company, Hartford, Conn. Quoted by Warkany.[7]
10 Illingworth, R. S. and Illingworth, C. M. (1966) *Lessons from Childhood*. E. & S. Livingstone Ltd., Edinburgh and London.
11 Peck, B. (1980) Should doctors salvage every life at any cost? *On Call*, *14*, 6.
12 Mawdsley, T., Rickham, P. P. and Roberts, J. R. (1967) The long term results of early operation on open myelomeningocele and encephalocele. *Br. Med. J.*, *1*, 663.
13 Mawdsley, T. (1981) From a study presented at a joint meeting of the Liverpool Medical Institution and the Liverpool Paediatric Club.
14 Lorber, J. (1971) Results of treatment of myelomeningocele. *Devl. Med. child Neurol.*, *13*, 279.
15 Lorber, J. (1973) Early results of selective treatment of spina bifida cystica. *Br. Med. J.*, *4*, 201.
16 Lister, J. and Orkiszewski, M. (1979) Myelomeningocele: An analysis of deaths following early closure of the back lesion. *Progr. in Ped. Surg.*, *13*, 75.
17 Habgood, J. (1980) *A Working Faith*. Darton, Longman & Todd, London, Chapter 19, 'Prolongation of life in the deformed newborn'.
18 Robards, M. F., Thomas, G. G. and Rosenbloom, L. (1975) Survival of infants with unoperated myeloceles. *Br. Med. J.*, *4*, 12.
19 Barclay, O. (1978) 'The nature of Christian morality' in *Law, Morality and the Bible* (Eds. B. N. Kaye and G. J. Wenham). IVP, Leicester.
20 This and the following paragraph owe a great deal to Packer, J. I., 'Situations and Principles' in *Law, Morality and the Bible*.[19]
21 Fletcher, Joseph (1966) *Situation Ethics*. SCM Press, London, p. 65.
22 Kidner, F. D. (1967) *Genesis*. Tyndale Old Testament Commentaries. Tyndale Press, London, p. 51.
23 E.g. Leviticus 21. 18-20.
24 Micah 4. 6, 7.
25 Isaiah 65. 20.
26 Acts 3. 8.
27 2 Samuel 4. 4.
28 Luke 14.
29 National Association of Mental Health Working Party (1971) *The Birth of an Abnormal Child: Telling the Parents*. *Lancet*, *2*, 1075.

[30] Pinkerton, P. (1970) Parental acceptance of the handicapped child. *Devl. Med. child Neurol., 12*, 207.
[31] Goodall, J. (1980) *Suffering in Childhood.* CMF Publications, London.
[32] Richards, M. P. M. and Robertson, N. R. C. (1978) in *Separation and Special Care Baby Units* (Clinics in Developmental Medicine, 68) (Eds. F. S. W. Brimblecombe, M. P. M. Richards and N. R. C. Roberton). Spastics International Medical Publications, Heinemann, London; Lippincott, Philadelphia.
[33] Warnock, M. (1978) *Report of a Committee of Enquiry into the Education of Handicapped Children and Young People. Special Educational Needs.* HMSO, London.
[34] Rosenbloom, L. (1980) Should handicapped children attend ordinary school? *Arch. Dis. Childh., 55*, 581.
[35] Mitchell, P. and Chalmers, I. (1980) Perinatal practice and compensation for handicap. *Br. Med. J., 281*, 868.
[36] Illingworth, R. (1980) Perinatal practice and compensation for handicap. *Br. Med. J., 281*, 1067.
[37] McGowan, M. P. (1980) Tailored advice and practical rehabilitation for families with a disabled child. *Lancet, 2*, 1018.
[38] Smithels, R. W., Sheppard, S., Schorah, C. J. *et al.* (1980) Folate deficiency and neural tube defects. *Lancet, 1*, 339.
[39] Laurence, K. M., James, N., Miller, M. *et. al.* (1980) Increased risk of recurrence of pregnancies complicated by fetal neural tube defects in mothers receiving poor diets, and the possible benefits of dietary counselling. *Br. Med. J., 281*, 1592.
[40] BMA (1981) *Handbook on Medical Ethics.* British Medical Association, London.
[41] Fletcher, John (1975) Moral and ethical problems of pre-natal diagnosis. *Clin. Genet., 8*, 251.
[42] Habgood, J. (1980) *A Working Faith.* Darton, Longman & Todd, London, Chapter 20, 'Ethical problems of screening for neural tube defects'.
[43] Kanner, L. (1964) *A History of the Care and Study of the Mentally Retarded.* Charles C. Thomas, Springfield, Ill.

CONGENITAL SUBNORMALITY

THE REHABILITATION OF THE
SEVERELY MENTALLY HANDICAPPED

DR. MED. JÜRGEN TROGISCH

Paediatrician, Katharinenhof, Grosshennersdorf, East Germany

Congenital Subnormality
The Rehabilitation of the Severely Mentally Handicapped

One morning about a month ago, before I left for my office at the Katharinenhof where I intended to put down on paper some of the ideas that had come to my mind as I prepared this paper, I found in the sitti ig room of our home a book by Elizabeth Kübler-Ross entitled *Leben bis unser Abschied*[6] which we might translate as 'Living with Dying'. My wife had borrowed this book from friends of ours to help her prepare a talk for the young people of our village on death and how to help the dying.

It contains an account of the death of a 5-year-old girl with an untreatable brain tumour. For about a year the mother had lived with the knowledge of the approaching death of her child. Divorced shortly before the diagnosis was established, she had had to cope with this burden completely alone until she met Mrs. Kübler-Ross. After the child had died her mother wrote to Mrs. Kübler-Ross: 'I am not afraid of death any longer, because I held Jamie in my arms when she died, and I didn't see anything frightening there. I no longer believe that death is the end, and even when I went away from the cemetery I didn't feel that I had left my child there. She was with me then just as she has often been with me since she died. Amid all the grief many beautiful memories of her remain and I shall always keep in my mind the recollection of her courage, cheerfulness and love. She was indeed a precious gift to me.'

I was greatly touched as I read these words, especially as I had come across them quite by chance. They recalled to my mind a passage from a very important book *Parents and their Mentally Retarded Child* by the Dutch theologian Paul Sporken.[12] He has established a number of parallels between the development of a positive attitude by parents towards their mentally retarded children and the stages of dying described by Kübler-Ross. Faced with the fact that their own child is mentally deficient, many parents come to a grave spiritual crisis. As they quickly realize the nature of the life-long burden that faces them, they often wish that their child could die. Sporken comments: 'Coming to terms with terminal illness is to accept something for which we can see an end. For the person concerned release comes with death itself; for the bereaved some time later. But coming to terms with the responsibility of caring for a disabled child is to accept a task for life.' In addition, the parents' concern about their disabled child's future is aggravated by the fact that they do not know how the child will manage after their own death.

This heavy and lifelong mental and physical burden, which nobody who has not experienced it can fully enter into, is that much worse when the children have severe deformities which need comprehensive and intensive nursing care.[11] Parents, and even skilled professional staff, may lose heart in the face of such severe disabilities. Failure to develop normally destroys even the feeblest rays of hope and prevents any possibility of rehabilitation. As a rule the parents have to undertake the soul-destroying and wearisome task of nursing care, and many a family has broken down under the strain. Very few could affirm with Jamie's mother, 'this child was indeed a precious gift to us'.

It is the problems presented by such children that I want to put before you now. In the first place, the very terms that are used to describe them by the different branches of the caring professions indicate the kind of feelings that exist, often subconsciously, towards this group of disabled people. They are

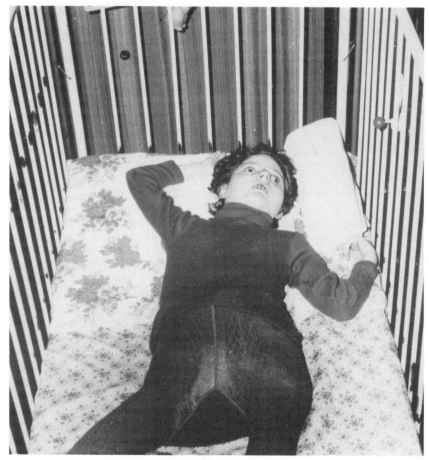

Fig. 1.

spoken of as totally ineducable, in need of care,[22] nursing cases, idiots, incapable of improvement, grossly mentally retarded, severely mentally disabled. As a rule, terms such as these are not applied in the context of rehabilitation.

Perhaps you are disappointed that I am not going to describe the outstanding results we have seen in our country in the rehabilitation of the blind and the partially-sighted, the deaf and the hard of hearing, those with speech and behaviour disorders, the physically handicapped and the mentally deficient. For all children with pre-, peri- and postnatal disablement a comprehensive (though still far from perfect) system of rehabilitation has been developed in the GDR, from antenatal diagnosis to the provision of social security and vocational training in adulthood. Five per cent of children in each school

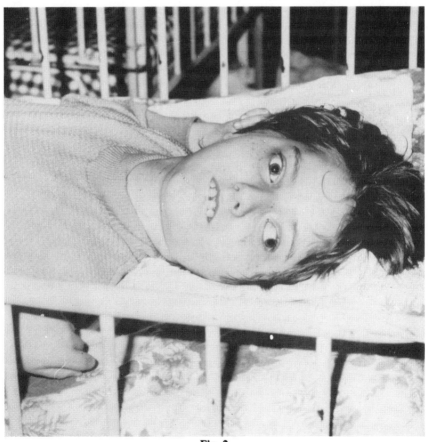

Fig. 2.

31

year—that is about 12,000 children annually—receive some form of free state assistance.[9] Somewhere between 100 and 200 children in each year of age in the GDR come into the category of severely mentally retarded.[14] 185 such children, young people and adults have found a home at the Katharinenhof, Grosshennersdorf, a rehabilitation centre run by the Home Mission of the Lutheran Church of Saxony (Evangelisch-Lutherische Landskirche Sachsens). I am going to tell you of some of the experiences that I, as a paediatrician, and my team have gained at the Katharinenhof. So that you can understand the situation better I should like to introduce you to two of our residents and, with the help of some illustrations, to take you to their bedsides.

This is Daniel (Fig. 1). He turns his head away because he does not know you, but most of the time he lies quite still and quiet in his bed. Most of the time he grips his right, spastically paralysed, hand in his left. The back of his head is flattened because he spends so much time lying on his back. His face is often pale and this is accentuated by his beautiful dark hair. Daniel cannot move his legs at all, and the bedclothes hold his feet in the footdrop position. When the nurses attend to his needs he often weeps.

Here (Fig. 2) he is looking serious. I sometimes have the feeling that he is looking right through me. Daniel is now 15 and he has been living with us at the Katharinenhof since he was three. These two pictures were taken shortly before he was transferred to the paediatric clinic with an infection which produced a high fever and massive vomiting. The extreme pallor of his complexion indicated the presence of a circulatory defect. He has now been in hospital for some weeks and his condition remains very serious. He must feel very lonely there in what are to him very strange surroundings, and the unpleasant procedures to which he is subjected, and which he does not understand, all combine to frighten him.

Now let us turn to Monika (Fig. 3). Like Daniel she lies in one position all day. Her hair conceals the very small and misshapen occiput. She seldom moves her arms and her thumbs are flexed inwards on to the palms of her hands. Her expression is vacant, but I'm glad she is looking at you in this picture. Both Daniel and Monika spend their lives surrounded by the white rails of their cots, and they often turn their gaze upwards to the white ceiling. Monika is 12 and has been in our home for seven years.

Their case notes read like this:

Daniel: Severe oligophrenia following pre- and perinatal brain damage. Spitz-Holter drainage at three months for hydrocephalus followed by three further operations to maintain clear drainage. Infantile cerebral palsy. Severe disuse osteoporosis. General atrophy.

Monika: Severe oligophrenia. Premature birth with congenital microcephalus, pre- and perinatal brain damage. Treatment-resistant infantile convulsions. Infantile cerebral palsy. Deformity due to malpresentation. Scoliosis of thoracic and lumbar spine.

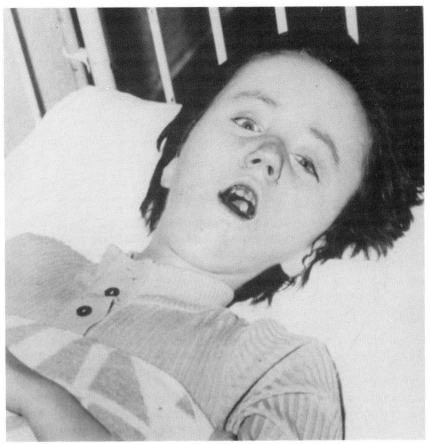

Fig. 3.

Meeting children like Daniel and Monika, and living with them, poses question upon question in many people's minds. Some people are afraid to meet them. Deep shock and sadness can often be seen on the faces of friends and relatives who visit them. Many a one has wept on leaving the room. Again and again long and serious discussion has arisen as people ask what possible meaning life can have for these severely disabled children.

I sometimes think that Daniel and Monika might ask questions too, if only they could. But neither of them can speak, so they cannot put their questions into words. But the questions are there nonetheless, even if we cannot hear them, and I should like to talk to you about some of the questions they raise, and try and translate them into language we can understand. These unspoken questions have been asked for a very long time in every home where such children are cared for, and we are constantly searching for solutions. Through some of the answers we have found already I want to try and give you an insight into the way we carry out our work among severely disabled people here at the Katharinenhof.

Daniel and Monika ask:
Why can't we live as comfortably as other children do in our country?
We lie in bed all day and in our room there are 12 more railed cots. In a corner near the door there is a bathtub which has to do service for all 23 children who live in our part of the house. There are wall cupboards over many of the cots with room for our pullovers and tights, but these have only been put up recently. The window sills are so high that we can't see out. The nurses are very fond of us but most of the time they are rushing about trying to get done at least the most important of their tasks.

Answers: The experiences of Scandinavian workers, who have found that severely mentally retarded people can live in an environment similar to that of a normal home,[1] have deeply influenced our thinking in the last ten years. We are therefore trying to make our institution less like a nursing home and more like a normal household. Up to now, comfort has usually been sacrificed to considerations of hygiene and the accepted pattern of daily nursing routine. As a result a very unimaginative environment has developed which has tended to restrict human contact to matters of general supervision, the provision of toilet facilities and other basic care. This corresponded closely to the traditional picture of the professional nursing sister.

When we recall what 'home' really means to us, and what we consider to be necessities of life in our own particular social sphere, we become uncomfortably aware of the contradiction between what we look on as legitimate requirements for ourselves and our children on the one hand, and what we, as representatives of society, are prepared to concede to handicapped people in permanent residential nursing homes on the other. From the conviction that life is very much more than the provision of nursing care, we have begun in a number of small ways to improve the living conditions in our home.[16] Unfortunately we have had to accept again and again that the living conditions in our caring institutions must depend on the degree of disability of the patients. The less a disabled person is able to look after himself, the further he is from being able to live a normal kind of life, compared with others of his own age.

Also, changes are only possible if the necessary additional financial resources are available. State support to our establishment, by means of regular *per capita* contributions, has increased threefold during the past ten years. This covers most of our running costs and without it our work could not continue. All new purchases, and the costs of improvements to our buildings, are paid for out of donations from 'friends' circles' and parishes.

34

Government funds do not cover these, but we have found that there is an increasing readiness to help.

Recent legislation in the GDR designed to improve the lot of handicapped people has brought a number of privileges to our residents, and we appreciate this very much. We are very pleased to be able to bring to fruition our plans for a new 72-bedded residential home for severely disabled patients. It is under construction at the moment and will help to reduce the extreme overcrowding we suffer from at present. The whole cost of the building is covered by donations from churches in the GFR, Switzerland and the GDR. When the new home is ready, Daniel and Monika will live there.

Daniel and Monika ask:

Why can't we be educated like all the other children in our country?

You may well ask if such severely disabled children can be educated at all, and what they should be taught. Both of these children can do some things that wouldn't be possible unless they had some learning ability, however small it may be.

Lying in bed Daniel can throw a ball with his left hand. Sometimes he grabs hold of his hair, or takes the nurse's hand and caresses himself with it. Again with his left hand he will throw everything out of his bed and open the wall cupboard that hangs above him. When he manages to do that he laughs, but only if there is nobody watching. When strangers are present he turns his head away.

Monika is quite relaxed and calm when she is moved out of the railed cot on to a mat, and she seems to like the postural exercises the physiotherapist helps her to perform. She is relaxed and contented when she hears someone singing, or when someone has the time to fondle her.

Answers: Observations such as these, and similar patterns of behaviour in other children as well as numerous experiments in the teaching of the severely mentally retarded, have made us realize that all severely disabled people have some learning ability. However, it is important that they are taken along a small step at a time and that we do not allow what has been achieved to be lost. Frequently it is our lack of knowledge or loss of sympathy with the patient, our failure to use our powers of observation and our unrealistic expectations, which hinder the further development of the learning process. Of course there are other adverse factors that are powerful deterrents to learning, such as an unfavourable environment and lack of staff. The most important opportunities for instruction and learning for the severely mentally disabled are during the daily nursing routine and through participating in, and helping with, the activities of others. Geriatric patients are in a similar situation. The English specialists, Dr. and Mrs. Günzburg, have called it 'second-hand activity'. [2][21]

The establishment of these learning functions will only be successful if nurses realize that they have to be teachers as well, and if all kinds of stimulatory activities are introduced into the nursing process. To have to rethink their role in such a way is difficult for staff who have been trained simply to be nurses, but it brings home to us again and again the fact that nursing by itself forces the patient into a passive role. We shall only make progress when actions performed for another person become activities undertaken *with* him. A similar re-evaluation of roles is taking place in the field of geriatrics.

Other important tasks, therefore, are added to the traditional functions of nursing care. These include: motivating the patient towards independence, especially in the activities of daily life; the conscious establishing of communication; using everyday activities such as washing, using a hair dryer, brushing, and rubbing ointment into pressure points, to encourage systematic stimulation of the sense organs. Again, in performing nursing duties such as turning, lifting and carrying the patient, one has to have regard for the principles of the physiotherapy of cerebral motor disturbances. Every nursing process can be looked on as the equivalent of physiotherapy in a normal life situation.[5]

Because they have had to rethink their role, the nursing personnel have become more ready to cooperate with colleagues in the other caring professions in helping mentally disabled people.[21] This was a necessary development, for no single branch of the specialized services that are involved could be expected to have the expertise to overcome all the problems met with in the care of the severely mentally retarded. Meanwhile, in many other countries, the state educational system is taking increasing responsibility for such severely disabled children and the first steps have been taken towards the preparation of a basic curriculum.[2 3 10 11] In the GDR the education and training of children with a high degree of mental subnormality is the responsibility of the Department of Health and Social Services. This education is called 'advancement'. Since, at the beginning of the 1970s, it became clear that these children were being excluded from every kind of learning activity and classified as incapable of 'advancement', their right to 'specific, quite distinctive and individually adjusted measures for rehabilitation care' was accepted[20] and incorporated into the 1977 Programme of Education for Teaching and Rehabilitation Institutions of the Department of Health and Social Services in the GDR.[20] This plan, which is now obligatory throughout our country, was worked out with the active participation of several caring institutions belonging to the church. The term 'rehabilitation care', which has been used in our home since 1971, is meant to cover not only the purely academic aspects; we take it to mean the total effort directed towards the rehabilitation of the severely mentally retarded.[14 16 18] There is, however, a wide gulf between the state of our knowledge and the actual possibilities of putting into practice what we have learned. However, there are many specialists who refuse to take up the opportunities guaranteed by law that are specifically directed towards the education and rehabilitation of the disabled.

Daniel and Monika ask:

Why do we find it so difficult to learn?

During her seven-year stay in our institution Monika has been ill 29 times with respiratory infections, including two occasions which were due to aspiration of vomit during epileptic seizures. The treatment of her epilepsy is always a problem and we have been unable to effect any improvement in her general atrophy or in her retarded growth and development. She has been treated three times for anti-convulsant rickets, while chronic constipation is yet another problem. Daniel has suffered many times from vomiting attacks due to infections and from the effects of his lack of mobility.

Answers: We all know by experience how much our efficiency is affected by acute or chronic illness. A slight subclinical influenzal infection could substantially prejudice our impressions of this Congress, and we are all well aware of this. But I notice constantly that, in practice, the connection between physical illness and learning ability is far too often disregarded. Apart from the unfavourable environmental factors that I have mentioned already, illness is, in my opinion, the most important element that hinders the learning process. Unlike ourselves, however, the severely mentally retarded are as helpless as babes and very young children in the face of all these hindrances to learning.

My wife and I have studied morbidity patterns at the Katharinenhof since 1974.[15 18] We have found that respiratory tract infections are by far the commonest cause of illness, accounting for 80% of total morbidity among the severely mentally retarded. Also important are dystrophies, iron-deficiency diseases, fluid balance disorders, chronic constipation and periodontal disease. We also have to be on the lookout for the so-called anti-convulsant rickets among our patients.

You will readily appreciate the demands that are placed on both personnel and equipment if we are to carry out even such simple prophylactic measures as getting our patients out into the fresh air each day, daily showers followed by cold therapy, getting them out of bed and out of their rooms in special invalid chairs or by other means, not to mention changing day and night clothes, changing the patients' position in bed under supervision, supplying orthopaedic appliances and continuously monitoring their use, and the daily systematic care of teeth and gums. In addition there is the individual administration of psychotropic and anti-epileptic drugs as well as the management of intercurrent chronic illness. Even the maintenance of minimum standards of hygiene needs constant supervision, as was clearly seen when a nine-month-old child contracted dysentery.

In spite of continuous improvement in our standards of care there are still important deficiencies, so that Daniel and Monika really are in a far worse situation than the healthy members of their age group.

Daniel and Monika ask:

Why is it that you often don't understand what we want and what we are trying to tell you?

Answers: It always astonishes me how, by careful observation and interpretation, sensitive parents and helpers *can* understand the needs of disabled people and how they are able to communicate with their children. If you try and analyse this form of communication, you find that it is very similar to the way a mother talks to her young baby.

This preverbal expression of the fundamental statement, 'I love you,' is a very important basis for communication with the severely disabled.[4] Added to this are verbal impressions conveyed by speaking or singing during the whole process of nursing care. A uniform precision in speech and a consistent attitude to the children by nurses and staff are vital if success is to be achieved. This applies equally to non-verbal communication through bodily contact, facial expression and voice and cadence. The sensory perception of smell, taste, temperature and touch play an important role in non-verbal communication. This can seldom be intentional or planned, but can be employed incidentally or subconsciously when speech is not possible.[4]

I think that we who have no disabilities have a real handicap in a situation like this which takes the form of an inability to communicate. We find self-control much more difficult than in the lingual-vocal field and without training and special experience this control, and the subsequent exercise of it, are very hard to achieve.[4] Changes in personnel will often destroy the bridges of understanding that have been built up between patient and nurse, however imperfect they may be, and such changes are disturbing and quite incomprehensible for the severely mentally retarded.

Daniel and Monika ask:

Why are we so alone?

Answers: When I compare the network of relationships that exists in the home between the children of a family and the adults who care for them with the situation in residential homes like ours, I am shocked by the great lack of attention given to the children in these homes. Also, when we take into account how little in the way of personal activity is possible for the disabled person, and his very considerable deficiencies in perception, we get some idea of the extent of his isolation.[4] This professional recognition of his need reminds me strongly of the cry of the paralysed man at the Pool of Bethesda, who said to Jesus, 'Sir, I have no one . . .', as we find it recorded in chapter 5 of John's Gospel. The consequences of isolation have now become generally known as a result of research into the effects on the personality of hospitalization and mental deprivation.[7]

Nowadays our remedies for behaviour disorders are psychotropic drugs, mechanical fixations and comprehensive behaviour and group therapy sessions. But the roots of these disorders lie wholly or in part in our lack of personal attention to these patients. Most of the time, disabled people like Daniel and Monika cannot even use bad behaviour as a means of attracting the attention of the overworked nurses, but we may have here an explanation for some of the instances of refusal of food or attacks of vomiting. We could probably overcome the staffing problem by introducing numbers of carefully selected lay helpers, but in our remote and rural surroundings such help is very limited. However, we have proved over a period of many years the value of temporary helpers during school holidays and the church's seasons of preparation, as well as one-day 'houseparent' assignments at the major festivals.

Daniel and Monika ask:
Why can't we come to the church services with you?

Answers: Daniel and Monika are both baptized but they are not welcome at our church services that follow the traditional pattern, because they disturb them. Everything that takes place at these services is beyond them; they do not understand, any more than do babies and young children who are not disabled. Director Bank-Mikkelsen from Denmark—one of the pioneers of the principle of 'normalization'—said at the Fourth Psychiatric Conference of the Home Mission held at Bad Saarow in 1974[1]: 'I take it as a principle that, whatever the circumstances, there should be a place where all people are treated as equals without respect of persons, that is, God's house where all souls are of equal value in spite of every human weakness.'

Severely handicapped people like Daniel and Monika can only be taken to a church service in a special ambulance and accompanied by a member of staff. We hold such a service at the Katharinenhof once a week, and I want to tell you about it because I think it is the most important development in our work with the severely mentally retarded, and is certainly the centre point of it all. Daniel and Monika only attend this service very infrequently—perhaps two or three times a year, but sometimes even not at all because of shortage of staff.

For this brief half-hour each child has a member of staff allotted to him who dresses him in his best clothes and takes him to the service. On entering the room where the service is held every child is greeted by name and shakes hands with the staff member who is leading the worship. At the beginning of the service a candle is lit on a tall candlestick so that everyone can see it. The candlestick stands alongside a screen which stretches right up to the ceiling and on this we project a coloured picture of a large cross throughout the whole time of the service. Unfortunately we have no chapel at the Katharinenhof, so we have to use a lecture room for our Sunday worship.

After the opening greetings a short piece of music is played on the flute or trombone, then the helpers sing the song 'God is so good' while the children are helped to clap their hands in accompaniment.   A very short prayer follows and then a simple creed is sung by all the helpers, which runs like this: 'Jesus loves me; he lay in the manger for me; he died on the cross for me; he rose from the grave for me; Jesus loves me'.

The proclamation of the gospel takes this form.   Each child is led to the altar by his nurse and the member of staff who is leading the service puts his hand on the child's head and blesses him with the words 'Jesus loves you,' caressing the child at the same time.   Meanwhile all the members of staff join in singing over and over again until all the children have returned to their places—'Jesus loves Katharine, Hallelujah.   Jesus loves Katharine, Halle-lujah'.   The first song of the service is then sung again, and again the children are helped to clap their hands in accompaniment.   Before the service comes to an end everybody joins hands.   The helpers arrange the hands of their children so that they reach the hands of the children sitting next to them, and the blessing is said together.   As the children leave and say goodbye, those who wish it are given a piece of chocolate or a sweet.   It would be wonderful if every severely mentally retarded child could take part in such a service of worship once a week.   Anyone who has taken part in such a service, and seen how the disabled behave, would agree.

Daniel and Monika ask:

Why are our parents so unhappy?   Why is it that they seldom, if ever, come to see us?

Answers: I tried to describe earlier some of the problems facing parents of a severely mentally disabled child.   We have to say repeatedly that most of the parents have not yet fully come to terms with the situation, as Sporken has indicated.[12]   As a rule parents are helpless in the face of this unavoidable suffering, and it is only in recent years that the experts have begun to understand how this process of 'acceptance' comes about and how parents can be helped towards it.   Nowadays the word rehabilitation is generally understood to mean the combined efforts of society to create for the disabled, as far as possible, a sense of human dignity in every area of their lives.   But in the case of the severely disabled and those with multiple disabilities the near relatives are themselves totally involved in this task that society has to perform on behalf of disabled people as a whole.   The entire family is often in need of rehabilitation, but with our present inadequate resources, both of staff and of time, we cannot tackle the problem satisfactorily.   This is all the more distressing as we now have very clear ideas as to how the parents could help,[17] while the expectatio1s which the parents have of us are constantly increasing.

Daniel and Monika ask:

What will happen when we are grown up and can no longer live at the Katharinenhof?

Answers: For more than ten years we have been making room for new intakes of children by transferring severely disabled adults to old people's homes and special psychiatric hospitals. But in spite of these efforts about 50% of all our children's beds are at present occupied by adults because there are no proper follow-up institutions for severely mentally retarded adults. We are filled more and more with sorrow and anxiety at the thought of having to remove these older patients away from the Katharinenhof. Time and again news has reached us of the death of one of our former patients shortly after the move has taken place, and it has usually been one of the most severely mentally retarded. One of our nurses said to me recently, 'None of our patients should be moved in future'.

At the Katharinenhof, in spite of unfavourable circumstances, we have laboriously built up the kind of environment in which our patients can feel comfortable, at least for the time being. In the many years that they spend with us they become accustomed to the rhythm of the daily, monthly and annual routine. They look forward to the various festivals of the year, the concerts, excursions and visits, and the many friends who come to help during the summer. Then suddenly, within a space of twenty-four hours, they are moved to a completely different environment where nobody understands what they are trying to say, and where their sense of isolation is as bad as it was at the beginning of the rehabilitation process. The sudden death of the disabled after such a move reminds me of the way elderly folk are liable to die shortly after they are admitted to an old people's home. They, too, are torn away from deeply established relationships, as a tree is uprooted in a storm. The non-disabled can often build up new relationships in such a situation, and so come to terms with it, but the severely mentally retarded person is a helpless prisoner of his circumstances. Ought we to say that we shall not move any more of our patients because of these unfortunate experiences? What are we to say to Daniel and Monika? They are almost at the age when they really ought to be moved.

Daniel and Monika ask their last question:

What is the point of living at all? Has our life any meaning?

Answers: I recently put a number of questions to the members of an introductory course which we run for new helpers at the Katharinenhof. Most of these people were already involved in the nursing of the severely mentally disabled. Two had come to us straight from school, but most had completed some form of professional training, although only two of them had any previous medical knowledge. Among the questions I put to these young adults, all of whom had been working with us for less than a year, was this: 'What changes have taken place in your life since you became totally involved with disabled people?' Here is a selection of their answers.

— For the first time in my life I feel I am doing something really significant.

41

— I feel I can now do things I wouldn't have thought myself capable of before.
— During my time here I have won the affection of Sabine—the child for whom I am personally responsible. Having had the opportunity to involve myself with a disabled person, I no longer think of her as disabled at all.
— Through constant association with disabled people I have become more familiar with their ways. From one isolated experience in the past I had imagined them as aggressive and pugnacious, but since I have begun to work with them I have found that my former opinion was wrong.
— I am more responsive now to human suffering and it arouses in me the desire to help.
— It's made me question what is really important in life.
— It has been an enriching experience. Work has assumed a new meaning and purpose. I feel I'm needed now.
— I've become more serious minded and think more consciously about life.
— In observing the disabled, I've discovered myself.
— I've learned to be patient and to appreciate even the slightest sign of progress.
— Through working with the disabled I've become more tolerant. My own little problems don't seem so important any longer, and I've learned to accept myself with all my own inadequacies. Above all I've learned to appreciate the little pleasures of life, such as the sight of a table laid for a meal, and especially I thank God that he has shown me that love can achieve more than hate or force.

Could not these be the answers to Daniel and Monika's last question? In the Charter of the 80s which was promulgated as a statement of intent by WHO to Rehabilitation International[23] we read these words: 'Rehabilitation is founded on the philosophy that what a person is able to do is more important than what he or she cannot do. It is an experiment in living based on the maximum use of all the abilities that everyone possesses.' Daniel and Monika have only very minimal abilities; some people would say that they have none at all. They both belong to the category of the disabled who cannot be rehabilitated because of the seriousness of their disabilities, as has been laid down by the Minister of Health of the GDR in an article published in a specialist journal.[13]

But when I consider how both Daniel and Monika, and other severely mentally disabled people, have by the very fact of their existence brought about such changes in the lives of the young people I have referred to, I am tempted to suggest that they ought to be employed as teachers in our educational system because of the effect they could have. The many and complex problems of acceptance of the disabled by society will only be solved gradually if the entire system of education and training within our society is prepared to take on this task as a firm and continuing commitment, and to incorporate it into the ordinary process of learning to grow up, from earliest childhood onwards.

The gap that exists between intention and reality can be illustrated by a quotation from the book *Good Morning, Beautiful—tape-recorded conversations* by Maxie Wander.[19] In a conversation with Rosie, a secretary, we find these words: 'Hitches are bound to arise, even in the simplest of human relationships. Faced with grief, or with someone who's dying, or a friend with cancer, we just don't want to know. It's the same with racial problems —I know what I'm talking about—or with someone who strays outside the usual norms of conduct in some way or other. A child was playing in our courtyard when it fell into a rainwater butt and was drowned. Everyone made great detours to avoid meeting the poor parents. They turned aside, or looked in the opposite direction, or talked a lot of nonsense. It was just a

Fig. 4.

43

way of expressing their inadequacy, but where do we get it from—this coward-
ice in the face of trouble?   Why are we so badly prepared for life; what *do*
we learn at school?'

Daniel and Monika may have achieved the fullest possible extent of their
rehabilitation a long time ago.   In reality it's us, the non-disabled, who are in
need of rehabilitation because we haven't learned to live with people like them.

Daniel and Monika have put nine questions to us.   They have called for a
high level of rehabilitation for themselves and for other severely disabled
people.   Their expectations of us[8] and of society at large are high in this
International Year of Disabled People.

Fig. 5.

I began this account on a personal note and I want to end with an experience that came to my mind when I was thinking about the theme of this Conference —'God's answer to the Disabled'. In my home region of Saxony we have a very beautiful Christmas custom which you may know of too; it is the erection of the Christmas pyramid. In a framework of wooden poles several storeys high a number of flat discs rotate, driven by the warm air from candles, and on these discs stand models of the well-known figures of the Nativity story. For some years now we have had a pyramid some five metres high standing in the courtyard of the Katharinenhof (Fig. 4). Before the figures are fixed on to the discs on the eve of Advent Sunday our staff take them to the bedsides of those children who cannot (or who could only with the greatest difficulty) be taken out to the pyramid in the courtyard. One year I carried the figure of Mary (Fig. 5) and as I stood by Daniel's and Monika's beds Mary looked at the children as they lay there. Suddenly it seemed to me that, in Daniel and Monika, I was seeing Jesus Christ lying in front of me in the railed cots of the Katharinenhof in Grosshennersdorf in 1978.

Could it be that Daniel and Monika have come into this world just for me? Are their deep and insistent questions perhaps God's questions to me? Are these two severely disabled children an answer—God's answer to me?

References

[1] Bank-Mikkelsen, N. E. (1974) Das Prinzip der Normalisierung in Einrichtungen für geistig Behinderte in *Bericht über die 4. Psychiatrische Fachkonferenz der Inneren Mission.* Information IV/74, Berlin, pp. 2-8.

[2] Dittman, W., Klöpfer, S. and Ruoff, E. (1979) *Zum Problem der pädogogischen Förderung schwerstbehinderter Kinder und Jugendlicher.* Rheinstetten.

[3] Fischer, D. (1978) *Zur Förderung Intensivgeistigbehinderter im Rahmen der Schule für Geistigbehinderte.* Bubenreuth.

[4] Fröhlich, A. D. (1974) Die Förderung schwerst (-körper)behinderter Kinder—Aspekte einer Kommunikationsförderung in *Bericht über die 4. Psychiatrische Fachkonferenz der Inneren Mission.* Information IV/74, Berlin, pp. 99-119.

[5] Fröhlich, A. D. (1980) De Pflege schwerst Mehrfachbehinderter als integrativer Bestandteil einer ganzheitlichen Förderung aus pädagogischer Sicht. *Deut. Krankenpflegezeitschrift, 1*, 41-44.

[6] Kübler-Ross, E. (1980) *Leben bis wir Abschied nehmen.* Stuttgart.

[7] Langmeier, J. and Matejczek, Z. (1977) *Psychische Deprivation im Kindesalter.* München.

[8] Presber, W. and Renker, K. (1981) Zum Internationalen Jahr der Geschädigten 1981. *Z. ges. Hyg., 27*, 93-97.

[9] Renker, K. (1981) Die medizinische und soziale Rehabilitation in der DDR. *Heilberufe, 33*, Beilage I-VIII.

[10] Schwager, H. J., Dreher, W. and Schorsch, S. (1980) Schwerstbehinderte. *Korrespondenzblatt Ev. Schulen u. Heime, 21*, 129-149.

[11] Speck, O. (1980) *Geistige Behinderung und Erziehung.* München.

[12] Sporken, P. (1975) *Eltern und ihr geistig behindertes Kind—Das Bejahungsproblem.* Düsseldorf.

[13] Tischendorf, R. (1981) Rehabilitation in der Deutschen Demokratischen Republik. *Z. ges. Hyg., 27*, 97-101.

[14] Trogisch, J. and Trogisch, U. (1977) Sind Förderungsunfähige 'nur' Pflegefälle? *Z. ärztl. Fortbild., 71*, 720-722.

[15] Trogisch, J. and Trogisch, U. (1978) Pflegerische und ärztliche Aufgaben in der Arbeit für geistig Schwerstbehinderte in *Bericht über die 7. Psychiatrische Fachkonferenz der Inneren Mission.* Information VII/77, Berlin, pp. 31-44.

[16] Trogisch, J. (1979) Anleitung zur Uberprüfung der Lebensbedingungen Geistigschwerstbehinderter in Dauereinrichtungen. *Zur Orientierung, 1,* 82-94.

[17] Trogisch, J. (1980) (unpublished) *Elternarbeit—Elternprobleme.*

[18] Trogisch, J. (1981) Arztliche Aufgaben bei der Rehabilitation geistig Schwerstbehinderter in *Die Förderung Schwerstbehinderter—Erfahrungen aus sieben Ländern* (Ed. A. D. Fröhlich). Luzern.

[19] Wander, M. (1978) *Guten Morgen, du Schöne. Protokolle nach Tonband.* Berlin.

[20] Bildungs- und Erziehungsprogramm für Rehabilitationspädogogische Förderungseinrichtungen des Gesundheits- und Sozialwesens der DDR—Teil I, Berlin, 1977.

[21] Interdisziplinare Zusammenarbeit in der Hilfe für geistig Schwerstbehinderte. *Zur Orientierung, 4,* 1979.

[22] Berichterstattung über Förderungseinrichtungen u.a. des Ministeriums für Gesundheitswesen der DDR. 1980.

[23] Deklaration der Charta für die 80er Jahre. (1981) *Z. ges. Hyg., 27,* 97-101.

REAL MAN THROUGH GOD'S GRACE*

RONALD WINTON, M.D., F.R.A.C.P.

*Chairman, International Congress of Christian Physicians.
Formerly Editor, Medical Journal of Australia.*

*Résumé of a paper presented to the ICCP Conference, Dresden, April 1981.

Real Man through God's Grace

Few of us would insist that we are physically and mentally perfect, though our limitations may not greatly bother us. We are very blind if we think we are morally perfect, and our moral imperfections are often more of a handicap than we realize. Spiritually we all fall short of our Creator's standards.

What did God mean Man to be? What is the Real Man, the Real Person? Listen to the voice of the Creator:

> 'Then God said: "Let us make man in our image, after our likeness; and let them have dominion over the fish of the sea, and over the birds of the air, and over the cattle, and over all the earth, and over every creeping thing that creeps upon the earth." So God created man in his own image, in the image of God he created him; male and female he created them.'[1]

God created man in his own image. Man so created was Real Man.

What does 'in his own image' mean? The Scriptures do not spell it out, and all sorts of attempts have been made to define it. We can point to capacities in man which mark him off from other creatures, and which would seem to correspond to divine attributes: reason, creativity, speech, moral responsibility, capacity to rule, and so on. There is something to be said for all these as indicating man's uniqueness, but it is questionable whether they provide a mark of the divine image.

Indeed there are dangers in seeing that image as conferring on man inherent qualities, and it is against the whole trend of the warnings in the Scriptures if we think of it as something in the very nature of man which puffs him up and makes him think that he is wonderful.

The essence of it seems to be just the opposite—not something inherently admirable in man, but the capacity to reflect God. This depends on a right relationship with God—a relationship of dependence. Sadly, it is a relationship that we tend to shy away from.

The first Adam succumbed to the lure put before him by the tempter, that he could become like God, knowing good and evil. This offered a state of independence and self-importance, instead of dependence upon God. This was different from being in the image of God and—on the face of it—much more attractive but it was all wrong. Man became like God, knowing good and evil, but his dream of power and independence proved to be illusory. In grasping at independence and life he had in fact chosen the way of defeat and death. Because of his disobedience, the vital relationship with God was broken; the image was marred. God shut man off from the tree of life and

Adam, expelled from Eden, could not return. Nevertheless, God still loved the creature he had made and had his own plans for him. A second Adam was to come.

Adam's dilemma is the dilemma of mankind, of us all, irrespective of how literally or otherwise we, as individuals, take the Genesis story. Modern man is frustrated and alienated in the manner of Adam. He has eaten of the tree of knowledge but the fruits of the tree of life continue to elude him. His desire may not be for eternal life (he may not believe in that) but for perfection in this life—physical, mental and social perfection. Often he finds God irrelevant, rejects him and the need for dependence on him, or simply denies his existence, either explicitly or in practical effect. As a result, man is left unutterably lonely in an imperfect and hostile world.

So man finds himself caught up in a conflict—within himself, with his fellow men and his environment, with God. The consequences are inevitable: personal frustration and inner conflict; mental and physical dysfunction; illness and disease; social problems and community strife; exploitation and despoiling of the natural environment; bitterness and quarrelling on the local scene and wars on the larger scene; suffering and, above all, death.

Man longs for something better. What he desires—though he may not know it or care to admit it—is to be a Real Person, as God meant him to be. But by himself he is powerless to re-enter Eden. God's holiness and justice are not to be denied. But neither may God's love be denied. So by his great grace, impelled by his inexorable love, he has made a way back for man at infinite cost to himself. He came among us, sharing our human nature and our life. In Jesus Christ the earth saw once more the image of God—God wholly revealed in terms of a human life. As our representative and substitute he suffered death for us. He rose again, conqueror over sin and death.

The image of God shines out, clear and splendid, in Christ and is reflected in those who look to him and trust him. 'We all,' writes St. Paul, 'with open face beholding as in a glass the glory of the Lord, are changed into the same image from glory to glory, even as by the Spirit of the Lord'.[2] The image of God, never actually lost, though sadly marred and faint, reappears in man. A right relationship is restored.

This may seem a far cry from the basic medical approach to handicap, from the question of how we as medical people can help the handicapped and of how God can help them through us. But we need to look behind the more obvious disabilities, and the problems they raise in a direct way. For behind the handicaps of some and the apparent well-being of others is the disability from which we all suffer, our alienation from God, the Creator, Life-giver and Life-sustainer. We must do all we can, with whatever expertise our particular place in medicine gives us, to help the handicapped to live as normally and as satisfyingly as possible. The compassion of Christ and the commitment to service which he lays upon us should double our motivation and our efforts to help and to heal. But mankind's greatest need is that healing of the spirit which we call reconciliation—reconciliation first to God, flowing over into reconciliation with our fellows, with the environment we live in, and with our own selves.

Perfection for man or for the disordered world is not yet. But we may even now know something of what it means to be a new creation in Christ and look forward eagerly to the day when God will fully restore all things, and we shall be changed into the glorious image of him who made us.

References

[1] Genesis 1. 26, 27.
[2] 2 Corinthians 3. 18.